THE
D-DAY
QUIZ BOOK

EUNICE WILSON

GRUB STREET · LONDON

Published by Grub Street, The Basement, 10 Chivalry Road,
London SW11 1HT

A catalogue for this title is available from the British Library

ISBN 0 898697 01 9

Typeset by BMD Graphics, Hemel Hempstead

Printed and bound by Biddles Ltd, Guildford and King's Lynn

ACKNOWLEDGEMENTS

Very many thanks to Terence Cuneo for permission to use his
painting; and to Capt Erik Gray, Ray Sturtivant, Norman Franks
and the pilots and ground staff of 247 (F) Squadron, in 83 Group,
2nd TAF in June 1944.

INTRODUCTION

The main object of any reference book is to tell you what you want to know about a subject and add to your knowledge by feeding in information that is interesting and exciting. This is what the *D-Day Quiz Book* will do. You may disagree with the choice of questions and answers. Why not? This is what an enquiring mind should do. But in this book you'll find four hundred questions which, it is hoped, will stimulate the mind in a fun way.

The compiler of this Quiz was nowhere near the beaches of D-Day, but she remembers very clearly the early morning skies dark with aircraft and loud with the song of engines, with the gliders passing over in silence. All the previous week the army had been rumbling through Stafford, going, unbelievably, in the 'wrong' direction. Not until years later was it realised that this was part of a grand deception and a major tactic of the overall plan. It is strange now for me to be living so close to where Montgomery first planned D-Day in a school that is no longer there, and where there is not even a blue plaque to say that 'here was planned the Day which changed our future'.

Eunice Wilson 1994

BIBLIOGRAPHY

Pegasus Bridge, Stephen E Ambrose, George Allen and Unwin, 1984.

Six Armies in Normandy, John Keegan, Jonathan Cape, 1982.

Overlord, Max Hastings, Michael Joseph, 1984.

From Apes to Warlords, Solly Zuckerman, Hamish Hamilton, 1978.

And the Walls Came Tumbling Down, Jack Fishman, John Hill, 1992.

The Dawn of D-Day, David Howarth, Collins, 1959.

Out of the Sky, Michael Hickey, Mills and Boon, 1979.

Call to Arms, Gen Sir Richard Gale, Hutchinson, 1968.

By Air to Battle, official account prepared for the Air Ministry by the Ministry of Information, Stephens, 1978. Originally HMSO, 1945.

Red Berets into Normandy, Huw Wheldon, Jarrold, 1982.

The Red Beret, Hilary Saunders, Michael Joseph, 1950 and New English Library, 1965.

The Red Devils, G G Norton, Leo Cooper, 1971.

The D-Day Landings, Philip Walker, William Kimber, 1980.

The Secrets of D-Day, Giles Perrault, translated by Len Ortzen, Corgi Books, 1966 and Arthur Barker, 1963.

The Longest Day, Cornelius Ryan, Victor Gollancz, 1960.

Invasion 44, John F Turner, Putnam, 1969.

The Right of the Line, John Terraine, Hodder and Stoughton, 1985.

Hand of Steel, Rupert Butler, Hamlyn, 1980.

Luftwaffe Handbook, Dr Alfred Price, Ian Allan, 1977.

Great Land Battles of World War II, Ian Hogg, Grub Street, 1987.

D-Day, Duncan Anderson, Magna Books, 1993.

D-Day – Operation Overlord, ed Tony Hall, Salamander, 1993.

D-Day, Dr Stephen Badsey, Tiger Books, International, 1993.

D-DAY QUIZ 1

1 What was the date of D-Day?

2 What was its code name?

3 Where were its primary arrangements originally planned?

4 What was the name of the Allied Air Force involved?

5 Which Airborne Division landed at Caen?

6 What was the name of the Exercise which had prepared the RAF for co-operation with the army in 1943?

7 Who was the UK Prime Minister at this time?

8 Who was the Supreme Allied Commander of Overlord and what nationality was he?

9 Who commanded the Allied Expeditionary Air Force?

10 Who commanded the 21st Army Group?

11 Where was the main area of the landing beaches?

12 Who was the Deputy Supreme Commander?

13 What was the first target date planned for the Invasion and what was it called?

14 Why was the date changed?

15 Who commanded the Allied Naval forces?

16 Where was the fatal rehearsal exercise in which nearly 1000 Americans were lost?

17 What was its code name?

18 Where were the Germans led to believe the Invasion would take place?

19 What was the name of the US Air Force involved in D-Day?

20 How did the name D-Day come about?

What's your score? _____10_____

1 What was the name of the Operation which launched the cross channel part of Overlord?

2 Why was the 2nd TAF so called?

3 Who were the enemy's chief army leaders?

4 What was the main type of glider used by the Allies?

5 What type of aircraft were the main ones which towed the gliders?

6 What were the main types of RAF fighters used for co-operation with the army and navy?

7 What were the radar stations called which were ranged along the south coast of Britain?

8 From which British regiment were drawn the first airborne soldiers, dropped on to the dropping zones in Europe on the 6th June?

9 Which were the main types of aircraft following the parachutists?

10 What were 'spoof' or 'feint' flights?

11 What was 'window'?

12 How many RAF squadrons provided the D-Day cover?

13 How long did it take to secure the main and initial beachheads?

14 Which was the main German Luftwaffe group in the D-Day area?

15 What was the other phrase used to describe D-Day?

16 Which of the RAF's main ground staff units were sent over to establish bases in France?

17 When did the first RAF aircraft begin operating in France following D-Day?

18 Within three weeks of D-Day, how many squadrons were operating in France?

19 What was the date of the plot to kill Hitler?

20 What was the Cab Rank system?

What's your score? _____

1   What was the German secret weapon, known before D-Day, with which the enemy hoped to make Britain surrender?

2   When was the first 'doodlebug' launched from France?

3   Which units were the first to spot them?

4   What was the new name given to Fighter Command to separate it from the Air Forces in Europe?

5   For what does SHAEF stand?

6   Roughly how many army divisions made the first assault?

7   With what were the English beaches in the South covered?

8   The joint Allied armies under General Montgomery were in one Group. What was its number?

9   What were the code names of the five beaches on which the Allies landed in Normandy?

10 Describe exactly where these beaches were to be found.

11 What were the code names of the ten British sections of their landing beaches?

12 On which beach did the Canadians land?

13 What was an LCT?

14 What was Mulberry?

15 Which was the area of the aircraft which the pilot called 'the office'?

16 In a transport aircraft who was the despatcher and what did he do?

17 Why did a paratrooper wear double thickness silk gloves?

18 What did the red light in an airborne troop carrier signify?

19 What was a DZ?

20 Which well known battleship was firing her guns as the gliders passed over her?

What's your score? _____

D-DAY QUIZ 4

1 Who was the noble lord who, accompanied by his personal piper, welcomed the paras on to the beach?

2 What is the name given to the bridge over the Caen and Orne Canal at Benouville which commemorates all airborne soldiers?

3 Which eight nationalities made up the Allied navies' combat vessel force on D-Day?

4 Thirty years after D-Day, Peter Vanneck was Lord Mayor of London. In what capacity had he served in Operation Overlord?

5 What was a Sapper?

6 What was an O – Group?

7 Which type of RAF ground attack aircraft took part in D-Day and after?

8 What was the name of Stanley Kubrick's film made about D-Day and on whose book was it based?

9 What was a Bangalore-Torpedo, carried by Allied Commandos and assault troops?

10 From what is Calvados made?

11 What did an RAF Beach Group do?

12 What day of the week was D-Day?

13 What was Rommel's wife's name and what for her was the significance of D-Day?

14 Where was the Allied Naval Operations Centre?

15 Where was kept the large model of the beaches which reproduced the invasion areas?

16 What was Operation Fortitude?

17 In what was it suspected that a spy was releasing clues to the enemy about the Invasion?

18 Who were the 'Bigots'?

19 Place in order by date, Torch, Overlord, Jubilee.

20 Who are/were the Red Devils?

What's your score? _____

1 Where is the Museum of the Airborne Forces?

2 What is the emblem of the Airborne Forces?

3 Were the Parachute Brigade all volunteers or were some drafted?

4 Where were the Airborne troops trained?

5 What was the Merville Battery?

6 Who led the 2nd Division of the British Airborne Forces?

7 What does SAS stand for?

8 Which RAF Group delivered them and supplied their operations?

9 Who was the GOC of the Airborne Division?

10 Who was his famous wife?

11 What was the other name of the Cherbourg Peninsula?

12 What was the popular name of the 1st Special Service Brigade?

13 Where in Britain was a similar terrain to Merville found and used for the planning and training involved in taking the Merville Battery?

14 Who designed the Gammon bomb, used for demolition or to destroy small vehicles, a small weapon which could go into a pocket?

15 Which company formed the army's Pathfinders during the D-Day Operation?

16 When was the first recorded attempt to re-supply ground troops by air?

17 From where in the UK did the RASC (Air Despatch) load and send their supplies?

18 With whom did they undertake flying training?

19 What is the regimental march past of the Parachute Regiment?

20 What is the German word for a tank?

What's your score? _____

1   When was 38 Group RAF formed?

2   Who opened the Museum of the Airborne Forces?

3   Which RAF Groups carried the 6th Airborne Division to Normandy?

4   What were the names of the three operations into which Overlord was divided?

5   Where is there a Memorial in the UK to the 22nd Independent Parachute Company?

6   What does it commemorate?

7   Which squadron of Albemarles towed Horsa gliders to crash land near the Merville Battery?

8   When the D-Day op was completed to what were 38 Group's activities switched?

9   What was the first plan for Overlord known as?

10   What was a Canloan officer?

11   What was a Bren?

12 What did the initials AVRE stand for?

13 Who commanded 2nd TAF – the Second Tactical Air Force?

14 Under whose Command was the formation FUSAG meant to deceive the enemy?

15 Where did the Germans think the fictitious formation was located?

16 How many gliders took part in Operation Mallard?

17 Which was the British phantom army?

18 What were the breakwaters for the Mulberry Harbour called?

19 What was meant by the code name Taxable?

20 What was the West Wall?

What's your score? _____

1 Name five RAF stations from where the gliders took off.

2 Who designed the badge to be worn on the sleeve of airborne soldiers?

3 Who created the bronze statue commissioned by the Trustees of the Airborne Forces Security Fund?

4 Who was Lord Byron's poetic hero who talked of 'Twas a summer's day – the 6th of June'?

5 What was the general code name for the Normandy beaches?

6 Who sent a pigeon back to say he had landed safely near St Lo and what was its significance?

7 For what did the initials COSSAC stand?

8 Who was the meteorologist who explained the weather situation for D-Day?

9 From which port to which port in the UK were the ships of D-Day harboured?

10 What unusual cargo did Stirling aircraft drop and what did the Germans call them?

11   Who was the first Allied soldier to be killed on D-Day?

12   In which town was von Rundstedt's HQ?

13   Where was the RAF's secret Y Service station in the most easterly point of southern Britain?

14   Which well known American writer was on the Omaha assault?

15   What was the name of General Bradley's command ship?

16   What was the purpose of a Filbert balloon?

17   Which RAF squadron flew the Glimmer radar spoof?

18   Which generals disapproved of the COSSAC plan?

19   Why?

20   Where is the Museum of Army Flying?

What's your score? _____

1 To which part of the British army do glider pilots belong?

2 How did fashionable women dress in France on and after D-Day 1944?

3 What was the women's fashion in Britain which made its appearance just before D-Day, first for those in active jobs, then as an essential item in the wardrobe?

4 What indicated the rank of an American private 1st class, a PFC?

5 What was a GI?

6 In which months were the first V-weapon attacks on Britain?

7 About how many men were in the British forces by 1944?

8 How many women?

9 What was the only US navy ship sunk by the enemy on 6 June 1944?

10 The Americans landed on Omaha Beach. What were the code names for its eight different sections?

11 On the 6th June, a coded message was put out by the BBC, 'The dice are on the table'. What did it mean?

12 A British submarine mission went in close to the French coast just before the landings. It involved two submarines to act as markers for the British and Canadian troops. What was its code name?

13 Operation Glimmer was the code word for what?

14 What words are best remembered by D-Day veterans who were on transport ships?

15 Name two beaches on which the Americans landed.

16 And the British?

17 Where in France was the first battle joined by Allied airborne troops?

18 What were 'crickets'?

19 Which bodies were considered to be expendable among the Airborne troops?

20 Who were the American father and son who landed on separate beaches on 6 June?

What's your score? _____

1 Which soldier announced to the world that the Allies had invaded France on D-Day?

2 Roughly how many anti-personnel and anti-marine mines had the Germans planted on the European shore? Was it: A) under 250,000; B) between 250,000 and 1 million; C) over 1 million?

3 Who was the German officer leading the naval action against the Allies?

4 What was the name of the Norwegian destroyer sunk with thirty casualties by a German E-Boat?

5 How long has the British army had vehicles with Caterpillar treads?

6 About how many Allied convoys and how many ships were involved in the D-Day invasion?

7 When was VE Day?

8 When was VJ Day?

9 What was the unofficial name for the assembly of ships as they got under way for France?

10 What types were the British ships in the vanguard to the Invasion?

11   Which US division was the first on the US beachhead?

12   Who commanded the German 6th Parachute Regiment on D-Day?

13   About how many Allied troops took part in the Normandy landings?
Was it: A) 1 million; B) 2 million; C) 3 million?

14   Where were dummy parachutists dropped?

15   What was the name of the German Military Intelligence?

16   Which was the Polish destroyer which took part in the Invasion?

17   What was the generic name for aircraft which towed gliders into battle?

18   Which sector of the beaches became known as 'Bloody Omaha'?

19   Why?

20   Roughly what was the total number of vehicles used in the first assault?

What's your score? _____

1   How long did it take the British to capture Caen?

2   What and where was Exercise Tiger?

3   Who appeared on Sword Beach to welcome the invading British troops?

4   In which Service did the present Queen Elizabeth serve in 1944?

5   What rank did she hold eventually?

6   With what local drink did the Invasion personnel toast Victory on the 6th of June?

7   What markings distinguished Allied aircraft from their Axis opponents?

8   What were the 6th Airborne's orders on taking the Orne Canal bridge?

9   Who relieved them?

10 What indicated the rank of a Lance Bombardier of the Royal Artillery?

11 What was issued to each officer and sergeant of assault infantry on D-Day to protect his official pocket watch in the event of a wet landing?

12 Who in England had to obtain special passes to get home?

13 How did gliders break away from their tugs?

14 Who was the official war reporter, the first to witness the opening of the Second Front?

15 When did the first V1 land on London?

16 What was the name of the BBC radio channel which broadcast general news?

17 When and where did the first V1 land?

18 Apart from news what else did the BBC broadcast which was important to Europe?

19 Which German army did the AEF engage in full on D-Day plus 3?

20 In which Service was the detective story writer Denis Wheatley, who helped to plan the deception around D-Day?

What's your score? _____

1 Where was the landing beach of Ouisterham?

2 What was the code name for the invasion of the south of France which coincided with D-Day?

3 What was the code name for the cover plan for Overlord?

4 What was Fortitude?

5 Who was the actor who stood in for and impersonated Monty at Gibraltar while the real Monty was in the UK for the final plan of D-Day?

6 When did he reveal his secret?

7 Leaflets were dropped on north-west France before D-Day. For what purpose?

8 Which Service was mainly a cover for female agents dropped into France?

9 Which was the first Allied airstrip to be constructed in Normandy and when?

10 A well-known war correspondent whose first name was the same as a British city accompanied the gliders. Who was he?

11 What was the arm badge worn by the 7th Armoured Division?

12 Which mythological figure rode the original Pegasus?

13 What was a flail?

14 Of what was 2nd TAF composed?

15 From which joint services exercise had they been formed?

16 When was 2nd TAF formed?

17 Why was John Colville, RAF, not allowed to fly beyond the British coast until after D-Day?

18 Three famous British battleships were part of the troop protection. Name them.

19 Which were the two main types of German aircraft in the dogfights over the beaches and beachheads?

20 Roughly how many RAF pilots, in percentage terms, were lost in that fateful June?

What's your score? _____

1   Which airfield was the first to be captured by the Allies just outside Caen?

2   What was the name of the cafe, the first place to be liberated from the Germans?

3   Which US film star was discharged from the army in June 1944?

4   Which famous personality signed his discharge papers?

5   What did the Allied commander of D-Day, Eisenhower, become after the war?

6   What did the slang word 'stonk' mean?

7   When did the Allies enter Rome?

8   Into what did Fighter Command temporarily lose its name?

9   When did the name Fighter Command re-appear?

10 How many squadrons of Typhoons had been formed by D-Day?

11 What was their main function?

12 What was the American designation for the US Mustang 111s as flown by the RAF?

13 What was the German jet fighter which appeared soon after D-Day?

14 Who commanded 2nd TAF in January 1944?

15 With whom did he have many policy disagreements?

16 What distinguished Monty's beret?

17 Where was the HQ of the 21st Army Group located?

18 What was a Stuka?

19 Where was the first Supreme Commanders' Conference held?

20 Who was the most famous person – ever – buried at Caen?

What's your score? _____

1   Bocage was the general name for the interior behind Caen. Why was it unsuitable for airfields?

2   Which German company designed the Tiger Tank?

3   What was the code word for the top level conference at St Pauls' School which Churchill attended?

4   Why was Coningham nicknamed Maori or Mary?

5   Which squadron attacked the Saumur railway tunnel two nights after D-Day?

6   Who coined the phrase 'Bodyguard of Lies'?

7   To which Group did the main fleet of Dakotas belong?

8   What did they do?

9   Who was in command of 83 Group's Control Centre?

10   144 Wing of 83 Group was the first RAF unit to operate from the French mainland.
Of which squadrons did it consist and who led it on D-Day?

11 From where in the UK did it operate?

12 What did GAF stand for?

13 What colours were the D-Day invasion stripes painted on Allied aircraft?

14 What were they for?

15 What is the full name today of the cafe, the first house to be liberated at Benouville on the 6 June and why is it so-called?

16 Who owns it?

17 Where was Rommel on D-Day?

18 Who was the operational commander of the two RAF Groups 38 and 46 involved in D-Day?

19 What are the two main towns on the Cotentin peninsula?

20 On what river is St Lo?

What's your score? _____

1 Which US divisions operated nearest to
   St Mere Eglise?

2 What was the British Commando's full title?

3 How were the gliders' take-off positions
   marked and called?

4 What was the main German position which
   had to be eliminated immediately by the
   6th Air Landing Brigade?

5 What was the name of the radar beacon used
   for the aircraft to home-in on?

6 What was the weather like on the nights of
   5/6 and 6/7 June?

7 By 6th June the number of operational
   fighter Groups had been reduced to how
   many?

8 How many active Sectors were there?

9 What were the clicking toys called which were
   used by soldiers identifying each other in the
   dark?

10 What had to be altered, physically and
   personally, before D-Day?

11 Where are the official British records of D-Day to be found?

12 What is the colour of the shoulder flash – badge – of the Airborne troops?

13 What colour are their berets?

14 What kind of photograph did RAF personnel carry with them?

15 Who wrote to whom that what was proposed for D-Day was 'the greatest thing we have ever attempted'?

16 Who was the BBC's Children's Hour character who impersonated Churchill for many of his radio speeches?

17 What was a forward observer?

18 Who was COSSAC?

19 What were the personal items that the general British public were specifically asked for in 1943?

20 What was the name of the islands off Utah beach on which US cavalry landed to destroy non-existent guns?

What's your score? _____

1 Why was Brittany too far away as a landing site?

2 Where was COSSAC's HQ?

3 How old was General Eisenhower when he became Supreme Commander?

4 Why was his appointment criticised?

5 Why were the Americans irked at the choice of subordinate commanders?

6 What was Karinhall?

7 The Americans and the Russians called the D-Day invasion by another name.
What was it?

8 Who commanded the American 1st Army?

9 Where was he born?

10 How old was he on his appointment?

11 Who was the German ace who flew more combat missions than anyone else?

12 Where in the UK was the 25 square mile area from which were evacuated the entire civilian

population so that the American assault forces could practice and rehearse the invasion with live ammunition?

13 What was the main difference in command between the USAAF and the RAF at this time?

14 From which country did the P-51 Mustang originate?

15 What engines did it carry?

16 What were its main roles?

17 Why was Leigh-Mallory, Air C-in-C for Overlord, disliked in some quarters?

18 Which part of England held the main concentration of troops and supplies for D-Day?

19 What was the US version of a Nissen hut?

20 What were the assembly areas nicknamed?

What's your score? _____

1 Lord Lovat and his Commandos had been on a big raid before in 1942. What was it?

2 What had Hitler said about Lovat in his death list – the list of people to be exterminated when he conquered Britain?

3 Who built the Atlantic and West Walls?

4 What happened to French girls who 'collaborated' and fraternised with the German troops?

5 Which is the museum nearest to where many of the land and air forces assembled?

6 At which museum will you find hundreds of photographs taken on D-Day?

7 What was a DUKW?

8 What was FUSAG?

9 What was an LST?

10 For what does REME stand?

11 What is T. O. T?

12 Name three British tanks of the period.

13 Name two German tanks.

14 With what was the Tommy's traditional tin hat covered? Why?

15 For what was Bayeux famous before the Invasion?

16 How many men was it suggested were needed to build the Mulberry Harbour?
Was it: A) under 10,000; B) under 50,000; C) over 50,000?

17 What was PLUTO?

18 How long did it take to construct?

19 What did Off Limits mean?

20 Which battle in the February before D-Day, provoked Churchill into saying 'we hoped to land a wild cat that would tear out the bowels of the Boche. Instead we have stranded a vast whale with its tail flopping about in the water'?

What's your score? _____

1 What was Radio Calais?

2 Who was court martialled for trying on his own initiative to talk the Germans into surrender?

3 What are the dates for the Battle of Caen breakout?

4 What were the nicknames of the RAF's Typhoon fighter aircraft?

5 Which was the only Allied jet fighter aircraft to enter service, very soon after D-Day?

6 How long did it take the Allies to finally defeat Germany?

7 On what date did British troops occupy Caen?

8 When did the Allies take St Lo?

9 When was Rommel wounded?

10 When did the Russians open their offensive on Germany?

11 What is significant about the 5th June?

12 Who was Eisenhower's Chief of Staff?

13 Of what did the 1st Special Service Brigade consist?

14 Who led the First Canadian Army?

15 Who led the First Polish Army Division?

16 Name five of the airfields on which the C-47s waited for take-off on the night on 5/6 June '44.

17 What were C-47s in civilian life?

18 What colour were invasion aircraft and what distinguishing marks did they carry?

19 At what height was it necessary for the Allied aircraft to fly to escape the enemy's radar?

20 On which date was the go-ahead for D-Day finally decided?

What's your score? _____

1 What overlooked the beach of La Breche where the 8th Infantry Brigade had the task of silencing the troops there?

2 Where did the 3rd Canadian Division practice with the 2nd in October 1943?

3 What was this operation called?

4 What were Bombardons?

5 What were Phoenixes?

6 What were Gooseberries?

7 Who was the famous painter who was killed with the 2nd Welsh Guards soon after the landings?

8 What had been his last work?

9 Where can you find more details of the Polish soldiers' part in the D-Day operations?

10 The 15th Scottish Division was part of the 21st British Army Group. When did they land in Normandy?

11 Who was General Eisenhower's British chauffeur?

12 What was the ultimate direction of the Allies after landing?

13 In spite of there being many Allied countries involved, which provided the launch pad for the Normandy Invasion?

14 What was the Allies' stated war aim?

15 Who wrote *The Longest Day*, in which there is a brief list of survivors?

16 At exactly what time did Operation Overlord officially begin?

17 Which Divisions formed the Pathfinders of the army?

18 What was their role?

19 Why was the Pas de Calais suspected by the Germans as being the focus of the Invasion?

20 By D-Day how many years had now elapsed since the beginning of the war?

What's your score? _____

1 What was Rommel's first name?

2 Why was Rommel appalled at what he saw when he made his inspection of the Atlantic Wall?

3 Who was Axis Sally?

4 What was the popular song she sang prior to D-Day which was so pertinent?

5 What kind of clothes did General Montgomery usually wear in place of regulation uniform?

6 To what German weapon did the British troops give the nickname 'Moaning Minnie'?

7 What are the cliffs called that meant home to British troops abroad?

8 Where was Hitler when D-Day started?

9 Who was Hitler's mistress?

10 What kind of food did Hitler prefer?

11 The French underground received their messages by what means?

12 Who was the French leader in Britain?

13 What were General Eisenhower's first names?

14 What did the Morse code – 3 dots and one dash, mean?

15 What was the piece of music played over British radio to encourage the underground movements in Europe?

16 The punks of the 1980s wore their hair in Iroqois style. Who adopted this style before them apart from the original Indians?

17 Who said: 'Two kinds of people are staying on this beach, the dead and those who are going to die. Let's get the hell out of here'?

18 What were the characteristics of the Dives Valley which made fighting difficult?

19 Who set off from this valley, in the 11th century on a similar mission but in reverse?

20 What were 'taping parties'?

What's your score? _____

1 Into which sea do the rivers Douvre and Vire run?

2 What was the German sign that warned of mines?

3 What were Rommel's asparagus?

4 What were S mines?

5 What was a 'stick'?

6 Which troops wore green berets?

7 Who was Lord Lovat's piper and what tune did he play on the beaches and beachheads?

8 With what did the war correspondents help to maintain their communications?

9 What was Brig General Teddy Roosevelt awarded after the landings on Utah Beach?

10 In order to provide every man of the assault forces with one ounce of sweets, two ounces of biscuits and one packet of chewing gum – what was the total needed?

11 About how long before D-Day was everything ready to go?

12 Who was the Commander-in-Chief of RAF Bomber Command?

13 Which was the only part of the United Kingdom to be occupied by the Germans?

14 What was the colloquial term for Eisenhower's rank?

15 How many British armoured regiments were equipped with the Crocodile tank?

16 What kind of tank was the Crocodile?

17 What is a Caterpillar?

18 2000 Norwegians were to be brought out of Sweden to Scotland in early 1944. There was a long discussion about how to complete this. Why?

19 What does FAC stand for?

20 What does Kaput mean?

What's your score? _____

NOTES

NOTES

NOTES

NOTES

ANSWERS D-DAY QUIZ 1

1   6 June 1944.

2   Operation Overlord.

3   St Paul's School, Hammersmith, London, which was Montgomery's HQ in May 1944, and incidentally where he had been a pupil.

4   Second Tactical Air Force – 2nd TAF.

5   The 6th Airborne.

6   The Spartan Exercise.

7   Winston Churchill.

8   General Dwight D Eisenhower, American.

9   Air Chief Marshal Sir Trafford Leigh-Mallory.

10 General Bernard Montgomery.

11 Normandy.

12 Air Chief Marshal A W Tedder.

13 1 June 1944 – D-Day.

14 The Invasion had to take place on a rising tide in daylight as near to dawn as possible and as soon after low-tide as practical, with a moon the night before. Only the 5th, 6th and 7th were now suitable. Bad weather was the main reason for cancellation.

15 Admiral Sir Bertram Ramsay.

16 Slapton Sands, Dorset.

17 Exercise Tiger.

18 In the Pas de Calais area.

19 9th Tactical Air Force.

20 Nobody really knows for sure. However, the main theory is that THE Day became D-Day – though there is much controversy about this. Deliverance Day, perhaps, or even D for Decision.

ANSWERS D-DAY QUIZ 2

1 Operation Neptune.

2 It was one which involved all the Allies in tactical co-operation with the Army. The 1st TAF was in N Africa, the 3rd was SEAC (South East Asia Command).

3 Field Marshals von Rundstedt and Rommel.

4 Horsa.

5 Albemarles and Stirlings. Four squadrons of each, Albemarles – 295, 296, 297 and 570. Stirlings – 190, 620, 196 and 299.

6 Typhoons, Spitfires and Mustangs.

7 Chain Home or CH, CH(EL) – extra low looking.

8 The Parachute Regiment.

9 Dakotas, Stirlings, and Halifaxes.

10 Mock flights designed to mislead, dropping 'window' not men, which confused radar and anti-aircraft, to divert attention.

11 Aluminium foil strips which interfered with German radar.

12 171.

13 One day.

14 Luftlotte 3.

15 The opening of the Second Front.

16 The Servicing Commando Units and the Construction Wings.

17 Four days later on the 10th June.

18 31.

19 20 July 1944.

20 A small formation of rocket-firing Typhoon aircraft operating over a battlefield and on call by forward ground controllers and ground troops to destroy enemy targets – eg, tanks in hull-down position – which presented particular difficulties for friendly artillery, tanks and infantry.

ANSWERS D-DAY QUIZ 3

1 Flying bombs launched from sites in northern France.

2 12 June 1944.

3 The Royal Observer Corps.

4 The Air Defence of Great Britain – or ADGB, 15 Nov 1943 till 15 Oct 1944.

5 Supreme Headquarters Allied Epeditionary Force.

6 37.

7 Rolls of barbed wire, mines and other tank obstacles.

8 21st Army Group.

9 Utah, Omaha, Gold, Juno and Sword.

10 Northern France from east of the Cherbourg Peninsula, Bayeux, Carpiquet to Caen.

11 Item, Jig, King, Love, Mike, Nan, Oboe, Peter, Queen and Roger.

12 Juno.

13 Landing Craft Tank.

14 'Temporary' floating harbours built on the beaches. It is interesting to note that bits of them are still there.

15 The cockpit.

16 The man who stood by the fuselage door of the troop carrier aircraft to assist paratroopers out and into the air, to be sure there were no snags.

17 To prevent burn as the ropes slipped through his hands.

18 That a paratrooper must make ready to jump, prior to a green.

19 A Dropping Zone.

20 HMS *Warspite*.

ANSWERS D-DAY QUIZ 4

1 Lord Lovat, Commando leader of the 1st Special Service Brigade.

2 Pegasus Bridge.

3 British, Canadian, American, French, Norwegian, Dutch, Polish, Greek.

4 Lt Commander of one of the MTBs.

5 A soldier of the Corps of Royal Engineers.

6 A small briefing to key personnel in the field, at which immediate orders were given.

7 Rocket-firing and bomber Typhoons (Bomphoons).

8 *The Longest Day* by Cornelius Ryan.

9 A weapon for demolishing walls and barbed wire entanglements.

10 Distilled cider apples, the main alcoholic drink of northern France.

11 Organise the distribution of materials for constructing airfields and provide defence for the beaches by barrage balloons.

12 Tuesday.

13 Lucie-Maria. It was her birthday.

14 Southwick House, Portsmouth.

15 At the Duke of York's Barracks, London.

16 The plan to feed false information to the enemy to make them believe the invasion would take place in the Pas de Calais.

17 The *Daily Telegraph*'s crossword puzzle in which, ostensibly by coincidence, clues were contained using the words Utah and Omaha, names of two of the US beachheads and also the code name Overlord.

18 Officers who were entrusted with the date and place of D-Day. They used special scrambler green telephones.

19 1) Jubilee – Dieppe raid – 19 Aug 1942.
2) Torch – the invasion of North Africa – 8 Nov 1942.
3) Overlord – D-Day – 6 June 1944.

20 The British Airborne Forces (6th Airborne Division) who were given the name by the Germans in Tunisia in December 1942 because of the colour of their berets.

ANSWERS D-DAY QUIZ 5

1   In the Browning Barracks at Aldershot.

2   Bellerophon's horse Pegasus.

3   They were all volunteers.

4   At RAF Ringway, later No 1 Parachute Training School, now Manchester's civil airport.

5   Seemingly indestructible fortress near Caen in France, protected by wide minefields and barbed wire, with guns deeply embedded in concrete. It was essential to the Allies that it should be destroyed.

6   General Richard Gale.

7   Special Air Service.

8   38 Group.

9   Lt Gen 'Boy' F A M Browning.

10 The novelist Daphne du Maurier, author of *Rebecca* and *Frenchman's Creek*.

11 The Cotentin Peninsula.

12   The Commandos.

13   Near Newbury, Berks.

14   Capt R J Gammon MC, 1st Parachute Batallion.

15   22nd Independent Company.

16   In 1916 when nine aircraft of the RFC flew 140 sorties in six days during the Siege of Kut al Amara, the Mesopotamian Campaign of WW1.

17   Swindon in Wiltshire, RASC comprised two units, No 36 Lines Communications Transport Column and 233 Army Group converted to air despatch duties, joined together for the task.

18   The RAF.

19   The Ride of the Valkyries, arranged by Donald Keeling and E F Rippon.

20   Panzerkraftwagen.

ANSWERS D-DAY QUIZ 6

1 15 Jan 1942.

2 Field Marshal the Viscount Bernard Montgomery of Alamein KG GCB DSO DL on 23 March 1969.

3 38 and 46.

4 Tonga – two parachute brigade ops in the early hours of 6 June; Mallard – main glider force in the evening of 6 June; Rob Roy – the re-supply mission.

5 At the end of what was the old runway at RAF Harwell, now part of the Atomic Energy Research Establishment.

6 Where the first soldiers and aircraft took off for the Invasion of Europe. An annual Service of Remembrance is held here by members of 38 Group and the Airborne Forces Association.

7 297 Sqn.

8 SAS (Special Air Service) and SOE (Special Operations Executive) operations.

9 Operation Cossac.

10 An officer of the Canadian army loaned to a British regiment.

11 A British light machine gun.

12 Armoured Vehicle Royal Engineers.

13 Air Marshal Sir Arthur Coningham.

14 General George S Patton, US 1st Army Group.

15 In Kent, Sussex and Essex.

16 256.

17 The British 4th Army which was supposed to be in Scotland under Lt General Sir A F A N Thorne, preparing to invade Norway.

18 Phoenix.

19 Radar decoy op to make the enemy think the invasion would be in the Pas de Calais area.

20 The extension of the Siegfried Line ordered by Hitler, 24 August 1944 when the pace of the Allied advance from the beachhead grew faster and wider.

ANSWERS D-DAY QUIZ 7

1 Tarrant Rushton, Harwell, Down Ampney, Brize Norton, Fairford.

2 Major Edward Seago in 1942.

3 Mrs A R Oxenford, sculptor, and accepted by the Royal Academy.

4 Don Juan.

5 The Far Shore.

6 Lt Noel Poole, an ex-Somerset bank clerk, with the SAS. He was the first to land.

7 Chief of Staff Supreme Allied Commander.

8 Gp Capt John Stagg.

9 Felixstowe to Milford Haven.

10 Two hundred life sized dummies of paratroopers as a diversion called 'dolls'.

11 Corporal Bonetard, an SAS trooper, who had been born in Brittany.

12 St Germain-en-Laye.

13 RAF Kingsdown, Foreland, Kent.

14 Ernest Hemingway.

15 USS *Augusta*.

16 It flew from RAF and naval launches, holding a 9 ft radar reflector which gave back an echo resembling a 10,000-ton attack transport.

17 218 squadron, dropping strips of silver 'window' to deceive the enemy's radar.

18 Eisenhower and Montgomery.

19 It was too small and made no allowance for the capture of the Cotentin Peninsula.

20 Middle Wallop in Hampshire.

ANSWERS D-DAY QUIZ 8

1   The Glider Pilots' Regiment.

2   In brightly coloured cotton dirndl skirts, high built up hair, and tall wooden platform shoes. To be as unlike the Germans as possible and as a gesture of defiance.

3   Slacks, costing about £4 a pair, and eight coupons.

4   A single inverted chevron worn on the upper arm of both sleeves.

5   An American soldier, standing for Government Issue. Generally of the lowest rank of private, but used to mean all enlisted men.

6   V1 – June 1944.   V2 – September 1944.

7   Four and a half million.

8   450,000.

9   The USS *Corry*. 13 members of the crew were killed, when it was hit by guns off Utah Beach.

10 Easy Fox, Fox Red, Fox Green, Charlie, Easy Green, Dog Green, Dog White, Dog Red.

11 It indicated the Red Plan for the French Underground to cut all phone and lines of communications for D-Day.

12 Operation Gambit.

13 A deception operation to make the Germans believe the Allies had already landed an invasion fleet off Boulogne on D-Day.

14 'Away all boats' and the Lord's Prayer.

15 Utah and Omaha.

16 Gold, and Sword. The Canadians landed on Juno.

17 At the Caen Canal and the Orne river bridges, by the 6th Airborne.

18 Small hand held metal toys, tin snappers, used to exchange identification signals. A single snap required two in answer. American troops added a pass word.

19 The hundreds of life size inflatable rubber paratrooper dolls dropped to mislead the enemy as delaying tactics.

20 General Theodore Roosevelt Jnr on Utah, and his son Captain Quentin Roosevelt on Omaha.

ANSWERS D-DAY QUIZ 9

1 Col Ernest Duphy, press attache to the Supreme Allied Commander, at 9.30 am on the 6th June.

2 B) It is said there were about half a million lethal devices.

3 Lt Cdr Heinrich Hoffman in an E-boat of the 5th Flotilla in the haze off the Normandy coast. Three ships attacked with 18 torpedos and retreated.

4 The *Svenner*.

5 Since 1928. There were treaded tanks in WW1 but they were not those made by the Caterpillar factory in California. The term now means, in general, vehicles with similar treads.

6 59 convoys, US navy records say 5,000 ships, British records say 4,500.

7 8 May 1945.

8 15 August 1945.

9 Piccadilly Circus.

10 Twelve minesweepers which cleared the waters at midnight on the 5th of June.

11 The 4th Infantry Division.

12 Baron von der Heydte.

13 C) Three million combat and support personnel of which 1.7 million were American.

14 Yvetot, 30 miles east of Le Havre.

15 The Abwehr.

16 The *Poiron* was part of the convoy defences which encircled the British and Canadian troops.

17 Tugs.

18 Dog Green.

19 It had the fiercest fighting and casualties were heavy and widespread.

20 20,111.

ANSWERS D-DAY QUIZ 10

1 More than six weeks.

2 The rehearsal for D-Day by American soldiers, off Slapton Sands, Dorset, which went disastrously wrong causing the deaths of almost a thousand men.

3 The Mayor of Colleville-sur-Orne, a village one mile inland, dressed in formal clothes and brass helmet.

4 The ATS, as Princess Elizabeth, a motor mechanic.

5 Second Lieutenant.

6 Calvados, apple brandy from Normandy.

7 Black and white invasion stripes on wings and fuselage.

8 'Hold until relieved'.

9 Lord Lovat's Commandos.

10 A single chevron on the upper arm of both sleeves.

11 A condom.

12 People who lived on the south coast of England who had not already been evacuated because they were in essential occupations.

13 If not by accident when the towing cable broke, when cast off by the release of the towing mechanism by the tug aircraft.

14 Douglas Worth.

15 The first V1s were launched against Britain on 12 June. The first to land on London was at Bethnal Green killing six people on the 13th.

16 The BBC Home Service.

17 At Swanscombe near Gravesend at 4.18 am on 13th June '44. The second at Cuckfield in Essex and the third at Bethnal Green all on the same day. The first to be shot down was on 14/15 June by Flt Lt J G Musgrave and his observer F/Sgt F W Samwell in a Mosquito of 605 Squadron.

18 Coded information and instructions to the Maquis and other units of the French Resistance.

19 The 7th Army.

20 In the RAF Volunteer Reserve.

ANSWERS D-DAY QUIZ 11

1   North east of Caen.

2   Anvil, later changed to Dragoon.

3   Bodyguard, formerly Jael.

4   The deceptional plan for the invasion of the Pas de Calais area.

5   M E Clifton-James who was in the Army Pay Corps in Scotland.

6   After the war in the filmed and ghosted story 'I was Monty's Double'.

7   They told French civilians that liberation was near and those living near the coast would have to move inland or, if not possible, to avoid the roads and move into open country.

8   The FANYs. First Aid Nursing Yeomanry.

9   On 7 June a landing strip was constructed at Asnelles, north east of Bayeux.

10   Chester Wilmot.

11   A Desert Rat.

12 Bellerophon.

13 A specially adapted tank fitted with whirling chains employed to clear a safe path through a minefield.

14 The Allied armies and airforces of 83, 84 and 2 Groups RAF, 38 Airborne Wing and 145 Photo Reconnaissance Squadron.

15 Exercise Spartan, Z and Composite Groups.

16 November 1943.

17 Because he was Churchill's private secretary and as such he knew the exact place and probable date of the invasion landings and his capture could not be risked.

18 *Rodney, Warspite* and *Belfast*.

19 Focke Wulf 190 and Messerschmitt 109.

20 Twenty-five percent of the RAF's strength.

ANSWERS D-DAY QUIZ 12

1 Carpiquet.

2 Cafe Gondrée, by paratroopers of the 6th
Brigade who were dropped into the town of
Benouville on the eve of D-Day to seize a
vital canal bridge.

3 Clark Gable.

4 Ronald Reagan.

5 President of the USA.

6 Artillery concentration – 'stonking' – shelling.

7 4 June 1944, two days before D-Day.

8 Air Defence of Great Britain and 2nd TAF.

9 15 October 1944.

10 26.

11 Army support and co-operation, radar station
demolition pre D-Day and train 'busting'
after.

12 P-51B and Cs.

13 ME 262 – photos were taken on July 25, 1944.

14 Air Marshal Sir Arthur Coningham KCB DSO MC DFC AFC who was later Commander of the Advanced Allied Expeditionary Air Force.

15 Sir Trafford Leigh Mallory.

16 He wore two badges on it: that of a General Officer and that of the Royal Tank Regiment.

17 Fort Southwick, Portsmouth.

18 JU 87 German fighter.

19 Norfolk House, St James Square, London, which was the Supreme HQ of the Allied Expeditionary Force – SHAEF.

20 William of Normandy, the Conqueror.

ANSWERS D-DAY QUIZ 13

1   It was too hilly an area, and too wooded, with narrow sunken lanes.

2   Porsche.

3   Exercise Thunderclap, on April 7, Good Friday.

4   He was a New Zealander. Maori was corrupted to Mary.

5   617 Squadron of Lancasters, CO Wg Cdr G L Cheshire.

6   Churchill, 'In wartime, truth is so precious that she should always be attended by a bodyguard of lies'. Thus the code name Bodyguard deceived the Germans into thinking the attack was to be at Pas de Calais.

7   46.

8   Carried troops, supplies etc and brought out the wounded.

9   AVM Sir Harry Broadhurst.

10 441, 442, and 443 RCAF, led by
Wg Cdr J E 'Johnnie' Johnson.

11 Ford near Arundel in Sussex.

12 German Air Force.

13 Black and white.

14 Mainly to distinguish Allied aircraft from the
enemy as so many nationalities were involved
but also so that the ground forces could
recognise them.

15 Pegasus Bridge Cafe, after the emblem of the
Airborne Forces.

16 Arlette Gondrée Pritchett, who inherited it
from her parents who had lived there since
1934.

17 At home for his wife's birthday.

18 AVM L N Hollinghurst, nicknamed 'Holly'.

19 Cherbourg and Caretan.

20 The Vire.

ANSWERS D-DAY QUIZ 14

1 82 and 101st.

2 1st Special Service Brigade.

3 By chalk number XXX.

4 The Merville Battery.

5 Eureka.

6 Much the same on both nights. Moonless with visibility of only 3 miles, cloudy and with 10-20 mph wind.

7 Four.

8 Reduced from 19 to 14, less than half those of 1941.

9 Crickets.

10 Moustaches had to be shaved off because they made those likely to be captured look too British.

11 The Public Record Office at Kew, mainly coded WO 219 and 205 and Leigh-Mallory's Diary in Air 37.

12 Light blue and maroon.

13 Maroon.

14 Small photographs taken in civvies which could be stuck to false identity papers if necessary to escape. (If you look at those of 247 Sqn taken at this time, they are all dressed in the same borrowed clothing!)

15 Churchill to Roosevelt 23 October 1943.

16 Larry the Lamb.

17 A gunner officer working with the infantry who was selecting artillery targets or an airman flying a Piper or an Auster at around 120 mph at 1000 ft.

18 COS – Chief of Staff – to the Supreme Allied Commander Lt General Frederick Morgan.

19 Holiday photographs taken pre-war on the Channel coasts of France and Belgium.

20 Iles St Marcouf – they had been duped.

ANSWERS D-DAY QUIZ 15

1 It was beyond the reach of effective air cover.

2 Norfolk House, St James Square, London.

3 53.

4 Because he had no battle experience and was said to have risen in rank too quickly.

5 The majority were British.

6 The Chief of the Luftwaffe, Herman Goering's estate.

7 The Second Front.

8 General Omar Bradley.

9 Missouri.

10 50.

11 Hans-Ulrich Rudel, German records say 2,530.

12 In west Devon between Appledore and Woolacombe.

13 The USAF was under army command and the RAF was independent.

14 America.

15 Rolls-Royce Packard/Merlins and Allisons.

16 Long-range escort, interception and ground attack.

17 Because of his supposed indecision, hesistancy and pessimism.

18 The South from Kent to Cornwall.

19 A Quonset hut.

20 Sausages, from their shape.

ANSWERS D-DAY QUIZ 16

1 Dieppe, 19 August 1942.

2 That he was a dangerous terrorist to be exterminated immediately.

3 Under Hitler's direction the Germans constructed a chain of forts similar to the Maginot Line, but running from Calais to the Atlantic coast. Slave labour and garrison troops were used in its construction.

4 Their heads were shaved, amongst other things.

5 The D-Day Museum at Shoreham on the English south coast.

6 The Imperial War Museum, London.

7 Commonly known as a Duck, a Duplex-Drive amphibious truck for landing men on the beaches.

8 First US Army Group, a fictitious army commanded by General Patton which was meant to mislead the Germans into thinking the Invasion would begin from the Essex area of the south-east and land in the Pas de Calais.

9 Landing Ship Tank.

10 Royal Electrical and Mechanical Engineers.

11 Time on Target.

12 Churchill, Centaur, Cromwell.

13 Tiger and Panther.

14 Green netting, so that branches and leaves could be stuck in it for camouflage.

15 The tapestry commemorating the Battle of Hastings, an invasion of Britain by the Normans in 1066.

16 B) – 45,000.

17 The Pipe Line Under The Ocean which pumped petrol direct from England to France.

18 41 days.

19 US equivalent of the British military's Out of Bounds.

20 Anzio in Italy.

ANSWERS D-DAY QUIZ 17

1 British run propaganda station whose main activity was to read out German prisoners' names.

2 The brother of a British Prime Minister, Lt William Douglas Home, a troop commander.

3 18-20 July '44.

4 Tiffie or Seven Ton Monster.

5 Gloster Meteor 1 which met enemy aircraft in July 1944.

6 One year until 8 May 1945.

7 10 July 1944.

8 18 July 1944.

9 17 July 1944.

10 22 June 1944.

11 It was the original date for D-Day but was postponed to the 6th because of bad weather.

12 General Walter Bedell Smith.

13 3, 4, 6 Commando and 45 Royal Marine
Commando.

14 Lt General H D G Crerar.

15 Maj-General S Maczek.

16 Membury, Greenham Common,
Aldermaston, and in Devon, Up Ottery and
Mumfield. In Lincolnshire – Cottesmore,
Spanhoe, Fulbeck, Saltby, Barkston Heath.

17 DC-3 airliners.

18 US aircraft were painted camouflage khaki,
the RAF green/grey, both with two black and
three broad white stripes on fuselage and
wing, the Allies' D-Day recognition
markings.

19 Below 500 feet.

20 4th June '44.

ANSWERS D-DAY QUIZ 18

1 The Casino of happier days.

2 Studland Bay, Dorset.

3 Pirate.

4 A chain of inflated rubber bags attached to the Mulberry harbours to absorb the force of the sea.

5 The hollow concrete barges used to anchor Mulberry.

6 Obsolete warships and others, sunk to the bottom of the sea which, with Phoenix, formed the walls of Mulberry.

7 Rex Whistler.

8 A room in the Pavilion at Brighton, where the Welsh Guards had been billetted.

9 At the Sikorski Institute, London.

10 14 June.

11 Kay Summersby.

12 East across France and the Low Countries, over the Rhine to Berlin.

13 Southern England.

14 To liberate Europe from the Nazis and to defeat Germany.

15 Cornelius Ryan in 1959.

16 15 minutes after midnight on 6 June 1944.

17 101st and 82nd American Airborne Division and the British 6th Airborne.

18 Mark the dropping zones for the paratroops and glider infantry.

19 It was the nearest point to the British coast and the narrowest part of the Channel.

20 Five years.

ANSWERS D-DAY QUIZ 19

1 Erwin.

2 It was incomplete, just as had been the Maginot Line.

3 The German propaganda singer on Radio Paris.

4 'I double dare you to come over here,
I double dare you to venture too near,
Take off your high hat and let's get friendly
Don't be a scare cat, say, what do you care
Can't you take a dare?'

5 Corduroy trousers, a roll neck grey sweater and his black beret with two badges.

6 The Nebelwerfer: a six-barrelled mortar.

7 The White Cliffs of Dover.

8 Asleep in his mountain retreat at Berchtesgarten.

9 Eva Braun.

10 Vegetarian.

11   By innocent sounding codes on the BBC's
      World Service.

12   General Charles de Gaulle.

13   Dwight David.

14   V (for Victory).

15   Beethoven's Fifth Symphony, the opening
      bars of which sound like this Morse message.

16   US Paratroopers.

17   Col George Taylor, CO of the US 16th
      Infantry Regiment to his men on Omaha
      Beach.

18   It was flooded deliberately by the Germans,
      but was swampy anyway.

19   William the Conqueror.

20   Parties of soldiers who removed mines and
      marked the cleared paths.

ANSWERS D-DAY QUIZ 20

1 The English Channel ... La Manche.

2 Skull and crossbones on a black background
   with Achtung Minen!

3 Lines of upright heavy posts hammered into
   a field to stop the gliders landing.

4 Mines that bounded into the air when stepped
   on scattering bullet-like ball bearings.

5 A batch of paratroopers or bombs ready to be
   dropped.

6 Lord Lovat's Special Service Brigade –
   Commandos.

7 William Millin; Blue Bonnets over the
   Border.

8 Carrier pigeons bought by Ronald Clark of
   United Press. Some reached the Ministry of
   Information, London in a few hours.

9 The Medal of Honor. He died soon
   afterwards of a heart attack.

10 6250 lbs of sweets, 12,500 lbs biscuits, and at
   least 100,000 packets of gum – more or less.

11 Seventeen days.

12 Air Marshal Sir Arthur Harris.

13 The Channel Islands.

14 A four-star general.

15 Two.

16 It was a flame-throwing specialised vehicle designed by General Sir Percy Hobart.

17 The tread which carries a tank forward.

18 Because the date set was too near to D-Day and spies might be infiltrated.

19 Forward Air Controller.

20 Finished.

TOP SELLING MILITARY BOOKS
FROM GRUB STREET